page 5

page 14

$$\frac{4}{5} \qquad \frac{5}{6} \qquad \frac{2}{3}$$

$$\frac{5}{7} \qquad \frac{3}{4} \qquad \frac{6}{8}$$

page 22

page 16

page 21

page 31

page 26

$$\frac{4}{5} \qquad \frac{5}{6}$$

$$\frac{2}{3} \qquad \frac{3}{4}$$

page 29

£2.25	89p
85p	£1.30
75p	£1.50

Extra stickers

Well done! Well done! Well done! Well done! Well done!

Leap Ahead

Leap Ahead Workbook

Maths

Home learning made fun

Key Stage 2
Maths

igloobooks

Numbers to 1000

Sam is an air-traffic controller. He must land the planes in the correct order. Match the information from the control tower with the numbers on the planes.

1. five hundred and four
2. eight hundred and seventy two
3. six hundred and twenty
4. five hundred and sixty five
5. one hundred and thirty two

a. 565
b. 872
c. 504
d. 132
e. 620

Write these flight numbers in words.

Flight 358 = _____

Flight 721 = _____

Flight 402 = _____

Flight 630 = _____

Answers on page 32

The flights last for different amounts of time. Flights to countries that are further away take longer. Flights usually run on time, but sometimes they arrive early or are a little delayed.

Complete this chart showing delays and early arrivals.

Flight number	Planned flight duration (mins)	Event	New flight duration (mins)
BA 248	480	+10 mins	490 mins
EJ 529	725	-100 mins	
AA 372	631	+100 mins	
SB 843	894	-10 mins	
KG 654	79	+10 mins	
BP 459	128	+100 mins	
GP 674	245	-10 mins	
FR 328	473	-100 mins	

Fill in the chart below with the correct flight times:

100 less	10 less	START	10 more	100 more
		648		

Answers on page 32

PARENT TIP: Practise saying numbers that are 1, 10 and 100 more or less than a given 3 digit number. Play a game. Mark a dice with +1, -1, +10, -10, +100, -100. Start on 500 and take turns to roll the dice and complete the calculation. The player with the largest number after an agreed number of rolls is the winner.

3

Order Numbers to 1000

Jack and Sammie work for the Post Office. They need to put these letters in order for delivery. Write each letter's number in sequence in the boxes below.

432 Green Lane

520 Green Lane

872 Green Lane

398 Green Lane

250 Green Lane

391 Green Lane

126 Green Lane

567 Green Lane

126 - ( ) - ( ) - ( ) - ( ) - ( ) - ( ) - ( )

The parcel vans have a delivery map. Join these parcels to their position on the number line below.

500   600   700   800   900   1000

600   750   975   525   850

Circle the largest number in each pair.

a   **b**   **c**   **d**   **e**   **f**

383, 349   635, 653   492, 421   556, 565   279, 229   736, 739

4

Answers on page 32

These parcels must be weighed to calculate postage. The weights come in multiples of 100, 10 and 1. Choose weight stickers to match these parcels.

a 265g — 200g 60g 5g

b 753g — 700g 50g 3g

c 482g — 400g 80g 2g

Complete these place value additions:

479 = 400 + ⬚ + 9

372 = ⬚ + 70 + ⬚

600 + 20 + 3 = ⬚

500 + ⬚ + 6 = 546

Answers on page 32

PARENT TIP: Practise partitioning and recombining numbers. This is an essential skill that your child will use later when adding and subtracting. Write multiples of 100, 10 and 1 on pieces of card and place them in sets, face down on the table. Take turns to choose one card from each set and recombine to make a 3 digit number.

Adding Numbers

These deep-sea divers are getting ready to go in the water.

Join their identity numbers to the correct air cylinder.

The air cylinder numbers need changing for the next set of divers.
Complete the sums below to find out the new numbers.

482 + 4 = [ ]

546 + 30 = [ ]

369 + 200 = [ ]

257 + 40 = [ ]

Answers on page 32

The team of deep-sea divers has been counting different types of fish they have seen this year.

bass	cod	eel	ray	turbot	sole
352	521	476	215	622	133

Calculate these combinations for their records.

Working out space.

bass + cod $\boxed{352}$ + $\boxed{521}$ = $\boxed{873}$

turbot + ray $\boxed{}$ + $\boxed{}$ = $\boxed{}$

cod + sole $\boxed{}$ + $\boxed{}$ = $\boxed{}$

eel + ray $\boxed{}$ + $\boxed{}$ = $\boxed{}$

Which fish did they see the most of? _____

Which fish did they see the least of? _____

How many more turbot did they see than cod? _____

Answers on page 32

erimeters

Farmer Ted needs to build new fencing around all of his fields. First he must calculate how much fencing is needed.

Field 1

He starts at one corner and walks around each side of the field marking down the measurements for each side. Then, he adds the measurements together to get the perimeter:
10m + 10m + 10m + 10m = 40m fencing.

Field 2

Work out the fencing needed for the other fields.

◯ + ◯ + ◯ + ◯ = ◯

Field 3

◯ + ◯ + ◯ = ◯

Field 4

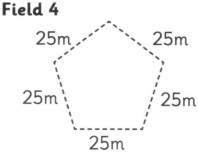

> **Working out space**

Field 5

> **Working out space**

Answers on page 32

Farmer Ted already has 100m of spare fencing.

Which 2 fields could he fix now? ....

How much more fencing does he need to order? ....

Draw 2 different fields below that each has a perimeter of 16cm.

Answers on page 32

PARENT TIP: Talk to your child about the perimeter being the distance around the edge of a shape. Find perimeters of objects around the house, such as picture frames, books and table mats. Try to include some shapes that are not four sided. Explain that shapes that appear bigger may not necessarily have the longest perimeter.

9

Pictograms

The recycling men have been sorting out the boxes they have collected from Fishpool Street.

Calculate the total number of boxes of each type.

Key: 🗑 = 5 boxes

		Total
Paper	🗑🗑🗑🗑🗑🗑	
Glass	🗑🗑🗑	
Plastic	🗑🗑🗑🗑🗑🗑🗑🗑	
Cardboard	🗑🗑🗑🗑	
Cans	🗑🗑	

Which item had the most collected? _____

How many boxes of glass were collected? _____

How much more paper was collected than cans? _____

Of which item were 20 boxes collected? _____

One van came back late and brought 5 boxes of glass and 10 boxes of cardboard. Draw this information in the pictogram.

Answers on page 32

10

Time Durations

Some roads have more houses and it takes longer for the recycling men to collect the boxes. Here are the start and finish times for each road. Work out how long it took to collect the boxes from each road.

Start	End	Time taken

Start	End	Time taken

Start	End	Time taken

Mersey Way is the final road for them to collect from. They start at 12.00 and they finish 20 minutes later. Show their final finish time on the clock face below.

Which road took the longest to collect from?

_____

Calculate how long it took the team to collect from all four roads. They began at 9.00 in Fishpool Street and finished when Mersey Way had been collected.

Total time taken = _____

11

Subtracting Numbers

Jacob works for a building firm. He is in charge of stock and must make sure they don't run out of equipment.

Equipment in stock on Monday:

bricks	tiles	pipes	switches	paint
957	876	387 metres	168	456 litres

On Friday, Jacob must change the stock list because some equipment has been used during the week. Calculate the remaining stock. Use the subtraction methods you have been taught in school.

bricks	tiles	pipes
957 in stock	876 in stock	387 metres in stock
300 used	50 used	3 metres used
Working out space	Working out space	Working out space

switches	paint
168 in stock	456 litres in stock
40 used	100 litres used
Working out space	Working out space

Answers on page 32

Lots of workers have been using nails. Jacob must subtract the amount each worker has used to calculate the number of nails left.

650 nails

MONDAY

John has used 50 nails

650 - 50 = [ ]

[ ] nails left

TUESDAY

Mick has used 100 nails

[ ] - 100 = [ ]

[ ] nails left

WEDNESDAY

Sam has used 6 nails

[ ] - 6 = [ ]

[ ] nails left

THURSDAY

Amanda has used 80 nails

[ ] - 80 = [ ]

[ ] nails left

FRIDAY

Bob has used 200 nails

[ ] - 200 = [ ]

[ ] nails left

Nails left at the end of the week = [ ]

Answers on page 32

PARENT TIP: Play a game. Have a target board drawn on paper with different numbered sections, e.g. 1, 5, 20, 45, 60. Roll a coin and see which number it lands on. Start on 200 and keep subtracting the numbers landed on. The first player to zero wins. Change the start number or the numbers on the target board to increase the difficulty.

Fractions

Follow the instructions to help Jasmine shade fractions of these shapes.

Colour in
$\frac{1}{6}$

Colour in
$\frac{1}{4}$

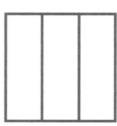

Colour in
$\frac{1}{3}$

Colour in
$\frac{1}{5}$

Colour in
$\frac{1}{8}$

Answers on page 32

Find the stickers with the correct answers to complete these additions.

a $\frac{1}{4} + \frac{2}{4} = $

b $\frac{2}{5} + \frac{2}{5} = $

c $\frac{1}{3} + \frac{1}{3} = $

d $\frac{3}{7} + \frac{2}{7} = $

e $\frac{4}{6} + \frac{1}{6} = $

f $\frac{4}{8} + \frac{2}{8} = $

14

Answers on page 32

These pirates are sharing the treasure. Circle the fraction of gold coins each pirate wants.

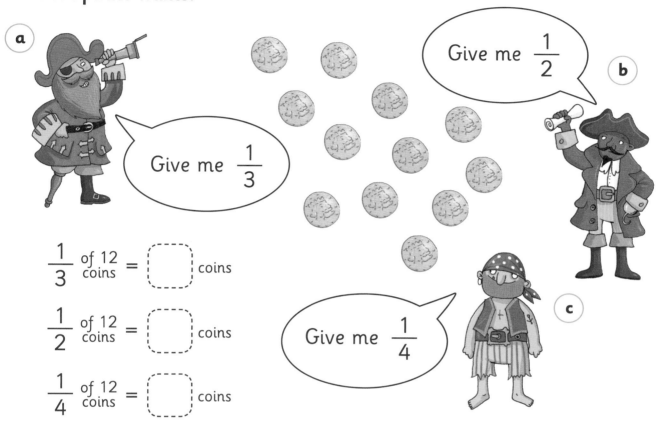

a Give me $\frac{1}{3}$

Give me $\frac{1}{2}$ **b**

Give me $\frac{1}{4}$ **c**

$\frac{1}{3}$ of 12 coins = ☐ coins

$\frac{1}{2}$ of 12 coins = ☐ coins

$\frac{1}{4}$ of 12 coins = ☐ coins

Are there enough coins to give each pirate the number he wants?

Answers on page 32

Colour $\frac{1}{2}$ of each pirate's flag. Make each flag look different.

Multiply by 3, 4 and 8

Stuart the mechanic has a delivery of new parts. The indicator bulbs are in packs of 3. Put the bulb stickers in the spaces below. Count in 3s to see how many have arrived.

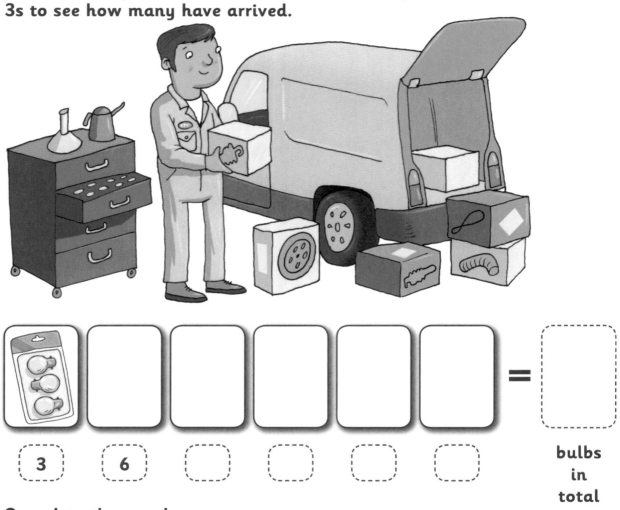

| 3 | 6 | | | | | = | bulbs in total |

Complete these orders:

Customer 1:
2 packs of 3 bulbs = ⬚ bulbs

Customer 2:
3 packs of 3 bulbs = ⬚ bulbs

Customer 3:
6 packs of 3 bulbs = ⬚ bulbs

Customer 4:
5 packs of 3 bulbs = ⬚ bulbs

The nuts and bolts have been split into 2 groups. How many are in each group?

⬚ nuts

⬚ bolts

In the tyre workshop, each car needs 4 new tyres.
Calculate the number of tyres needed each day.

	Monday	Tuesday	Wednesday	Thursday	Friday
Numbers of cars	6	3	8	4	5
Tyres needed	6 x 4 = 24				

Some cars have arrived for a service. They need to have new spark plugs.

4-cylinder cars need 4 spark plugs each.

☐ spark plugs

8-cylinder cars need 8 spark plugs each.

☐ spark plugs

Complete this number sequence and solve the multiplications.

8 ☐ ☐ 32 ☐ ☐ 56 ☐ ☐ 80

3 x 8 = ☐   6 x 8 = ☐   4 x 8 = ☐

5 x 8 = ☐   7 x 8 = ☐   9 x 8 = ☐

Answers on page 32

Measures

Amy and Calum work on the Space Station measuring things they find in outer space.

Amy measured the width of these craters in centimetres, but Calum measured them in metres. Join Calum's measurements to the correct craters. Circle the widest crater.

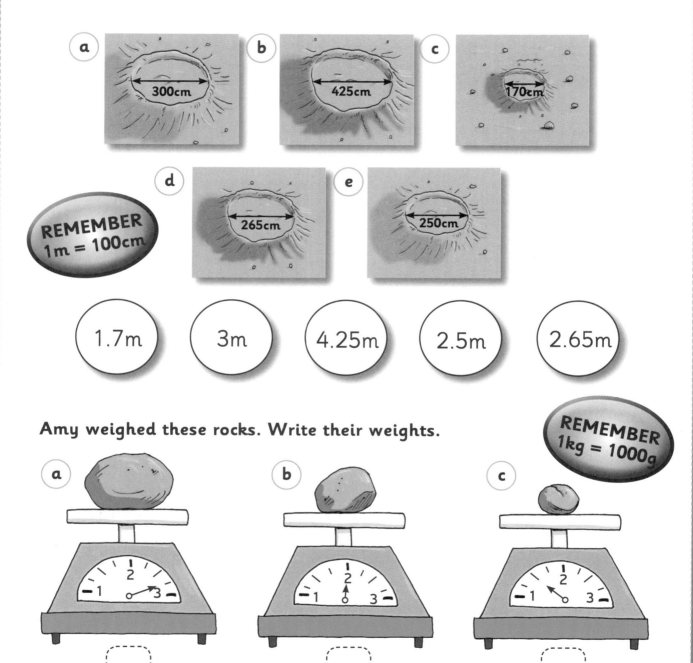

a 300cm

b 425cm

c 170cm

REMEMBER
1m = 100cm

d 265cm

e 250cm

1.7m   3m   4.25m   2.5m   2.65m

Amy weighed these rocks. Write their weights.

REMEMBER
1kg = 1000g

a _____ kg

b _____ kg

c _____ kg

Circle the heaviest rock.

Answers on page 32

Calum has measured the length of some icicles. He needs to add some of the lengths together. Can you help him?

a 20cm + 41cm = ⬚   **b** 35cm + 22cm = ⬚

c 150cm + 34cm = ⬚   **d** 245cm + 20cm = ⬚

d 325cm + 75cm = ⬚   **f** 62cm + 27cm = ⬚

The last job for Amy was to melt some of the icicles and measure the amount of liquid that resulted. Write the measurements.

Jug 1   Jug 2   Jug 3

⬚ ml   ⬚ ml   ⬚ ml

Calculate the capacity difference between:

Jug 3 and Jug 1   ⬚ ml - ⬚ ml = ⬚

Jug 1 and Jug 2   ⬚ ml - ⬚ ml = ⬚

Answers on page 32

PARENT TIP: Your child needs to understand and use the relationship between centimetres and metres. Write some measurements on card, including equivalent pairs, e.g. 250cm and 2.5m. Put them face down, then take turns to select two cards. If they are a pair, keep them. If not, return them to the table. The player to find the most pairs is the winner.

19

Multiplication

These cattle ranchers have to move hundreds of cattle to new land for the winter. Use the grid method to calculate the cattle in each group.

3 fields with 26 cattle in each

(a)

x	20	6
3	60 + 18 = 78	

2 fields with 34 cattle in each

(b)

x	30	4
2	( ) + ( ) = ( )	

4 fields with 17 cattle in each

(c)

x	10	7
4	( ) + ( ) = ( )	

5 fields with 24 cattle in each

(d)

x	20	4
5	( ) + ( ) = ( )	

They need to carry enough water for the trip. For one day they need 26 litres. Work out how much they need for 2, 4 and 8 day trips. You can use doubling to help you.

2 day trip

4 day trip

8 day trip

Answers on page 32

The cattle ranchers split themselves into small groups and arrange to meet at various times during the trip.

Some wear digital watches, others have clock faces (analogue).
Join the equivalent times.

a 5:45

b

c 3:30

d

f

e 4:00

i

g 8:15

h 10:20

j

Answers on page 32

Find analogue clock stickers to match each of these times.

6:40

9:10

2:15

Angles

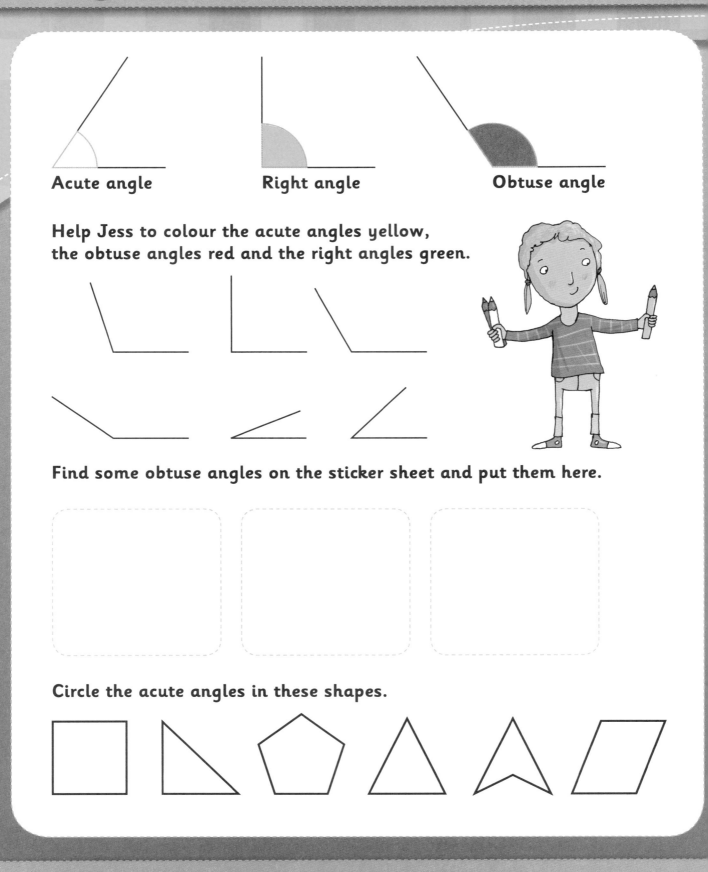

Acute angle   **Right angle**   **Obtuse angle**

Help Jess to colour the acute angles yellow,
the obtuse angles red and the right angles green.

Find some obtuse angles on the sticker sheet and put them here.

Circle the acute angles in these shapes.

PARENT TIP: Go on an angle hunt. Look around the house for different types of angles. Make a right angle tester by tearing off the corner of a sheet of paper and use it to check the angles. An angle smaller than the square corner is an acute angle, bigger means it is obtuse. Show your findings on a bar graph. Which type of angle did you see the most of?

Lines

Aaron has forgotten to use coloured lines when drawing his picture.

Use a ruler and felt-tip pens to draw over the lines in the right colours.

green (horizontal)

blue (vertical)

red (parallel)

Help Aaron find his way through the maze from a to b using horizontal and vertical lines. Draw lines to mark his pathway.

Count the number of each type of line that you have used.

Horizontal =

Vertical=

Could you have done it using fewer lines?

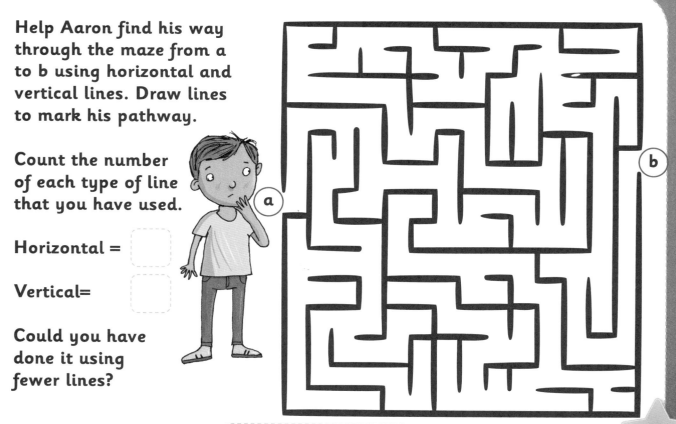

Answers on page 32

Division

Ben the greengrocer is sorting the fruit and vegetables into small groups. Help by circling the groups and calculating the answer.

How many 3s in 12?

$12 \div 3 =$ ( )

How many 2s in 14?

$14 \div 2 =$ ( )

How many 4s in 20?

$20 \div 4 =$ ( )

How many 5s in 25?

$25 \div 5 =$ ( )

Complete some more divisions. Count up in steps to find the answer.

$21 \div 3 =$ [7]

$32 \div 4 =$ [ ] $35 \div 5 =$ [ ]

$16 \div 4 =$ [ ] $18 \div 2 =$ [ ]

$24 \div 4 =$ [ ] $15 \div 3 =$ [ ]

How many 3s in 21?
3, 6, 9, 12, 15, 18, 21...there are seven 3s in 21!

Answers on page 32

Ben puts up some posters to help when he sorts the fruit into groups.

Look at the number triangles below. Write two multiplication sentences and two division sentences that use the 3 numbers on the triangle.

E.g.

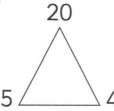

20

5 / \ 4

| 5 x 4 = 20 | 4 x 5 = 20 |
| 20 ÷ 4 = 5 | 20 ÷ 5 = 4 |

a

3

6 / \ 18

b

5

30 / \ 6

c

4

28 / \ 7

d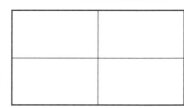

8

16 / \ 2

Ben discovers that some of the groupings cannot use up all the fruit.

Solve these divisions, then circle those with a remainder of 2.

a 17 ÷ 5 = ☐ r ☐   **b** 9 ÷ 2 = ☐ r ☐

c 28 ÷ 3 = ☐ r ☐   **d** 22 ÷ 4 = ☐ r ☐

e 42 ÷ 10 = ☐ r ☐

Answers on page 32

More Fractions

Peter and Molly have some fraction tasks to do. They need to write the equivalent fractions for these pairs of shapes. Work out these fractions.

$$\frac{1}{4} \qquad \frac{2}{8}$$

Find the fractions stickers and put them in order of size.

Complete this sequence.

$$\frac{1}{10}, \frac{2}{10}, \boxed{}, \boxed{}, \frac{5}{10}, \boxed{}, \frac{7}{10}, \boxed{}, \boxed{}, \frac{10}{10}$$

Circle the fraction equal to $\frac{1}{2}$.

Answers on page 32

The fractions in the two boxes below have lost their partners.
Use the fraction wall to help you join pairs of equivalent fractions.

1											
$\frac{1}{2}$						$\frac{1}{2}$					
$\frac{1}{3}$			$\frac{1}{3}$				$\frac{1}{3}$				
$\frac{1}{4}$			$\frac{1}{4}$			$\frac{1}{4}$			$\frac{1}{4}$		
$\frac{1}{6}$		$\frac{1}{6}$		$\frac{1}{6}$		$\frac{1}{6}$		$\frac{1}{6}$		$\frac{1}{6}$	
$\frac{1}{12}$	$\frac{1}{12}$	$\frac{1}{12}$	$\frac{1}{12}$	$\frac{1}{12}$	$\frac{1}{12}$	$\frac{1}{12}$	$\frac{1}{12}$	$\frac{1}{12}$	$\frac{1}{12}$	$\frac{1}{12}$	$\frac{1}{12}$

$\frac{1}{3}$	$\frac{1}{6}$	$\frac{3}{4}$
$\boxed{\frac{2}{6}}$	$\frac{1}{2}$	$\frac{3}{12}$

$\frac{1}{4}$	$\frac{2}{12}$	$\frac{2}{4}$
$\frac{4}{12}$	$\frac{9}{12}$	$\boxed{\frac{1}{3}}$

Think up 4 other equivalent fraction pairs.

Find answers of these fraction sums:

$\frac{2}{3}$ of 6 = ☐ $\frac{3}{4}$ of 8 = ☐ $\frac{4}{5}$ of 15 = ☐

Answers on page 32

PARENT TIP: Use buttons or pieces of pasta to help your child split quantities into fractions, e.g. to find 4/5 of 15 get 15 buttons and share into 5 groups explaining that each group is 1/5. Now push 4 of those groups together to create 4/5. Count the buttons to find 4/5 of 15.

Money

Mr Zandini runs the travelling circus. There are acrobats, clowns and fire jugglers. People pay to watch the show.

Here are the costs:

	Front rows	At the side	Back rows
Adult	£3.50	£3.00	£2.50
Child	£2.50	£2.00	£1.50

Calculate the total cost and change needed for the families below.

a

We want seats at the side, please.

Total Cost =
Change from £10.00 =

b

We want seats at the front, please.

Total Cost =
Change from £10.00 =

c

We want seats at the back, please.

Total Cost =
Change from £10.00 =

d

We want seats at the front, please.

Total Cost =
Change from £20.00 =

Calculate the total cost for your family to go to the show. Compare the cost for each of the 3 seating positions. Which seats will you choose?

Answers on page 32

The ice-cream seller has run out of change. People must pay with the exact money. Help these people choose the right coins to pay with. Circle those coins.

Need to pay £4.50

Need to pay £3.20

Need to pay £2.75

The price of some of the snacks has been reduced. Calculate the new prices, find the new price sticker.

Popcorn	£3.75	£1.50 off
Choc bar	99p	10p off
Water	£1.00	15p off
Fizzy pop	£1.50	20p off
Crisps	80p	5p off
Hot dog	£2.25	75p off

Answers on page 32

Data Handling

Zak the zookeeper is delivering food to some of the animal enclosures.

He has put the food required onto trolleys in the warehouse.

Complete the table to help Zak record the food that has been used today.

	Tins	Bottles	Boxes	Bags
Lions	5	2	3	4
Penguins				
Elephants				
Monkeys				
TOTAL				

Which type of food has been used the most today: tins, bottles, boxes

or bags? _____

How many tins were used? _____

Of which food type were 8 used? _____

How many fewer bottles than boxes were used? _____

Answers on page 32

Zak checks the number of animals in each enclosure to make sure none have escaped. He records the results in a bar chart.

How many monkeys are there? ....

Calculate the number of lions and elephants. ....

How many more penguins than lions are there? ....

Zak also counted 16 meerkats and 11 snakes. Add this information to the bar chart by colouring bars for the meerkats and for the snakes. Find the meerkat and snakes stickers and put them here.

How many animals in total did Zak count? ....

Answers on page 32

PARENT TIP: Your child needs experience looking at data presented in different ways, such as tables, tallies, pictograms and bar charts. They also need to collect data and present it themselves in a variety of ways. Ask friends and family questions about favourites and write down their choices as a tally. Then present this information as a simple bar chart.

Answers

Page 2: Numbers to 100
1-c, 2-b, 3-e, 4-a, 5-d

Page 3: 10 and 100 More and Less
EJ529 = 625 mins, AA372 = 731 mins,
SB843 = 884 mins, KG654 = 89 mins,
BP459 = 228 mins, GP674 = 235 mins,
FR328 = 373 mins

Page 4: Compare and Order to 1000
126 - 250 - 391 - 398 - 432 - 520 - 567 - 872
a=383, b=653, c=492, d=565, e=279, f=739

Page 5: Place Value to 1000
scales b= 700g + 50g + 3g
scales c = 400g + 80 g + 2g

479 = 400 + 70 + 9, 372 = 300 + 70 + 2,
600 + 20 + 3 = 623, 500 + 40 + 6 = 546

Page 6: Adding Numbers
yellow diver = tank c, blue diver = tank d, purple diver = tank a,
orange diver = tank b
a: 482 + 4 = 486
b: 546 + 30 = 576
c: 369 + 200 = 569
d: 257 + 40 = 297

Page 7
Bass + Cod: 352 + 521 = 873
Turbot + ray: 622 + 215 = 837
Cod + Sole: 521 + 133 = 654
Eel + Ray: 476 + 215 = 691

1: Turbot, 2: Sole, 3: 101

Page 8: Perimetres
field 2: 50m, field 3: 60m, field 4: 125m, field 5: 100m
Page 9
Farmer Ted could fix field 1 and 3 or 1 and 2.
Farmer Ted needs to order 275m of fencing.

Page 10: Pictograms
Paper = 30 boxes, Glass = 15 boxes, Plastic 40 boxes, Cardboard
= 20 boxes, Cans = 10 boxes

Plastic
15 boxes of glass was collected.
20 boxes more paper than cans.
Cardboard.

Page 11: Time Durations
Fishpool Street: Time taken is 30 mins, Driftwood Close: time
taken is 45 mins, Boundary Road: Time taken 15 mins
Mersey way is finished at 20 minutes past 12.
Driftwood Close took the longest to collect from.
Total time = 3 hours 20 minutes

Page 12: Subtracting Numbers
657 bricks left, 826 tiles left, 384 metres of pipe left, 128
switches left, 356 litres of paint left
Page 13
There are 214 nails left at the end of the week

Page 14: Fractions
a= 3/4, b=4/5, c=2/3, d=5/7, e=5/6, f=6/8

Page 15
pirate a wants 4 gold coins, pirate b wants 6 gold coins, pirate c
wants 3 gold coins
There isn't enough to give them all what they want.

Page 16: Multiply by 3, 4 and 8
18 bulbs in total.
customer 1 = 6 bulbs, customer 2 = 9 bulbs,
customer 3 = 18 bulbs, customer 4 = 15 bulbs
12 nuts and 20 bolts.
Page 17
Tuesday = 12 tyres, Wednesday = 32 tyres,
Thursday = 16 tyres, Friday = 20 tyres
28 spark plugs, 48 spark plugs
3x8=24, 6x8=48, 4x8=32, 5x8=40, 7x8=56, 9x8=72

Page 18: Measures
crater a = 3m, crater b = 4.25m, crater c = 1.7m, crater d =
2.65m, crater e = 2.5m, Crater b is the widest.
rock a = 2.75kg, rock b = 2kg, rock c = 1.5 kg
Rock a is the heaviest.
Page 19:
a = 61cm, b = 57cm, c= 184cm, d = 265cm,
e = 400cm, f = 89cm
Jug 1 = 450ml, jug 2 = 250ml, jug 3= = 850ml
jug 3 - jug 1 = 400ml, jug 1 - jug 2 = 200ml

Page 20: Multiplication
b = 68 cattle, c = 68 cattle, d = 120 cattle
2 day trip = 52 litres, 4 day trip = 104 litres,
8 day trip = 208 litres

Page 21: Analogue and Digital Time
a-i, b-e, c-j, d-g, f-h

Page 23: Lines
horizontal lines = 18, vertical lines = 19

Page 24: Division
12÷3=4, 14÷2=7, 20÷4=5, 25÷5=5
21÷3=7, 32÷4=8, 35÷5=7,16÷4=4, 18÷2=9, 24÷4=6, 15÷3=5
Page 25
triangle a: 6x3=18, 3x6=18, 18÷3=6, 18÷6=3
triangle b: 5x6=30, 6x5=30, 30÷5=6, 30÷6=5
triangle c: 4x7=28, 7x4=28, 28÷4=7, 28÷7=4
triangle a: 2x8=16, 8x2=16, 16÷2=8, 16÷8=2
sums a, d and e have remainders of 2.

Page 26: More Fractions
5/10 = 1/2
Page 27
2/3 of 6= 4, 3/4 of 8=6, 4/5 of 15=12

Page 28: Money
Family a=£9 (£1 change), Family b=£9.50 (50p change),
Family c=£8 (£2 change), Family d=£17 (£3 change)
Page 29
Popcorn=£2.25, Choc bar=£89p, Water=85p,
Fizzy pop=£1.30, Crisps=75p, Hot dog=£1.50

Page 30: Data Handling
Boxes have been used the most, 9 tins were used, bags, 5.
Page 31
8 monkeys, 14 lions and elephants, 8, 63 animals